# B.C.
# Loneliness is
# Rotting on a
# Bookrack

## Johnny Hart

**CORONET BOOKS**
Hodder Fawcett, London

Copyright © 1972, 1973 Publishers
Newspaper Syndicate

Copyright © 1978 CBS Publications,
The Consumer Publishing Division of
CBS, Inc.

First published by Fawcett Publications
Inc., 1978

*Coronet edition 1979*

---

Printed in Great Britain for Hodder
Fawcett Ltd., Mill Road, Dunton Green,
Sevenoaks, Kent (Editorial Office: 47
Bedford Square, London, WC1 3DP) by
Hunt Barnard Printing Ltd.,
Aylesbury, Bucks.

ISBN 0 340 23473 3

7.3

7.4

RATCHET
RATCHET
RATCHET
RATCHET
RATCHET
RATCHET
RATCHET
RATCHET
RATCHET
RATCHET
RATCHET

7·11

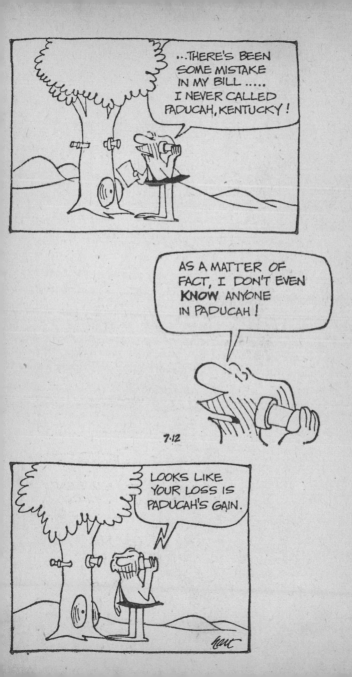

SCREECH

7.13

7·24

7-25

7·29

8·1

8·5

87

3

8:11

8·17

9-22

9.23

BWANG

9.2

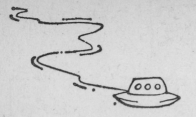

918

9.16

5

RR
CROSSING

R R

10-7

10·13

10.16

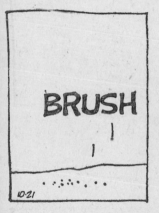

11·2

11·3

TOUGH LUCK, KID, THE COMPUTER PREDICTS A VICTORY OVER YOU BY A MARGIN OF 60%.

11·4

WELL,..UH, CONGRATULATIONS AND GOOD LUCK.
...THE WHAT?

7

11-21

11·23

11·24

12·21

8

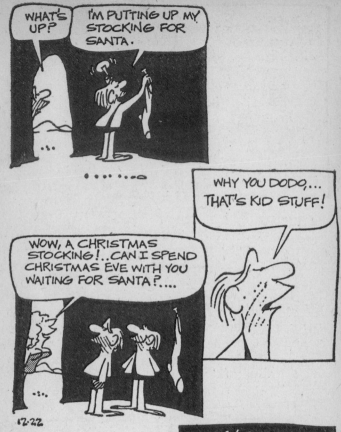

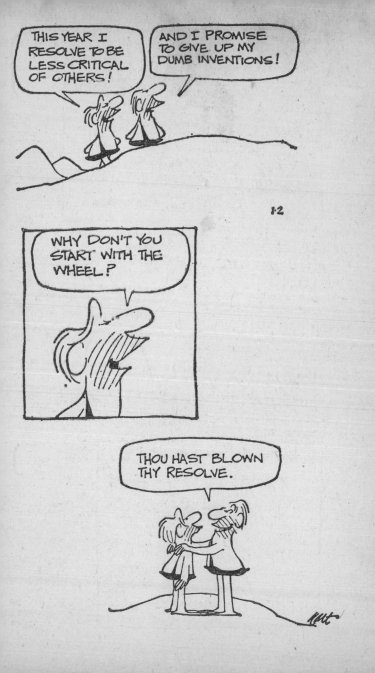

1·3

# ALSO AVAILABLE IN CORONET BOOKS

### JOHNNY HART

### JOHNNY HART & BRANT PARKER

### CHARLES M. SCHULZ

*All these books are available at your local bookshop or newsagent, or can be ordered direct from the publisher. Just tick the titles you want and fill in the form below.*

Prices and availability subject to change without notice.

---

CORONET BOOKS, P.O. Box 11, Falmouth, Cornwall.

Please send cheque or postal order, and allow the following for postage and packing:

U.K. – One book 22p plus 10p per copy for each additional book ordered, up to a maximum of 82p.

B.F.P.O. and EIRE – 22p for the first book plus 10p per copy for the next 6 books, thereafter 4p per book.

OTHER OVERSEAS CUSTOMERS – 30p for the first book and 10p per copy for each additional book.

Name ...................................................................................................

Address ...............................................................................................

.............................................................................................................